S0-ASN-383

Written by Sue Graves
Illustrated by Alison Atkins
Designed by Blue Sunflower Creative

Language consultant: Betty Root

This is a Parragon Publishing book
First published in 2004

Parragon Publishing
Queen Street House
4 Queen Street
Bath, BA1 1HE, UK

ISBN 1-40543-005-2
Printed in China

A Tiger for Toby

p

Notes for Parents

Reading with your child is an enjoyable and rewarding experience. These **Gold Stars** reading books encourage and support children who are learning to read.

The **Gold Stars** reading books are filled with fun stories, familiar vocabulary, and amusing pictures. Sharing these books with your child will ensure that reading is fun. It is important, at this early stage, for children to enjoy reading and succeed. Success creates confidence.

Starting to read

Start by reading the book aloud to your child, taking time to talk about the pictures. This will help your child see that pictures often give clues about the story.

Over a period of time, try to read the same book several times so that your child becomes familiar with the story and the words and phrases. Gradually your child will want to read the book aloud with you. It helps to run your finger under the words as you say them.

Occasionally, stop and encourage your child to continue reading aloud without you. Join in again when your child needs help. This is the next step toward helping your child become an independent reader.

Finally, your child will be ready to read alone. Listen carefully to your child and give plenty of praise. Remember to make reading an enjoyable experience.

Using your Gold Stars stickers

You can use the **Gold Stars** stickers at the back of the book as a reward for effort as well as achievement. Learning to read is an exciting challenge for every child.

Remember these four important stages:

- Read the story **to** your child.
- Read the story **with** your child.
- Encourage your child to read **to you**.
- Listen to your child read **alone**.

7

It was Tuesday morning.
Toby was very excited.

He was going to the pet shop.

He was going to the pet shop
to buy a pet.

"What pet should we buy?"
asked Mom.

"Let's buy an elephant," said Toby.

"Oh no," said Mom. "An
elephant is too big."

11

Toby saw a book. The book
was about a hippo.

"Let's buy a hippo," said Toby.

"Oh no," said Mom. "A hippo is too fat."

Toby saw a snake. The snake was long and wiggly.

"Let's buy a snake," said Toby.

"Oh no," said Mom. "A snake
is too long and wiggly."

Just then Toby saw a man. The man was dressed as a lion.

"Let's buy a lion," said Toby.

"Oh no," said Mom. "A lion would make too much noise."

Toby and his mom got to the pet shop. Toby saw a boy. The boy had a toy tiger.

"Let's buy a tiger," said Toby.
"A tiger would be the best pet."

Toby and his mom went into the pet shop. They saw lots of pets.

There were big pets and small pets. There were fat pets and thin pets. But there were no tigers at all.

"Well," said Toby, "these pets are good. But a tiger would be better."

"But we can't have a tiger," said Mom.

"Wait here," said the man.

The man went to the back room

He came back with a basket of kittens.

There were black kittens. There were white kittens. And there was one small, striped kitten.

"This kitten is called Tiger," said the man. "Would you like Tiger for a pet?"

"Oh yes," said Toby. He gave
Tiger a hug. "Tiger is the best
pet of all."

Read these words. Look back in the book and find the words.

Toby

Mom

elephant

hippo

lion

kitten

29

Gold Stars reading books are for children who are beginning to read.

- Familiar, repeated vocabulary
- Short sentences
- Large, clear type
- Pictures that support the text
- Review activity